JANNIE'S REHAB FOR

FITNESS AND CLEAN EATING

Workbook

By

JANNIE EDDINS

Copyright © 2018 JANNIE EDDINS

Disclaimer

All the material contained in this book is provided for educational and informational purposes only. No responsibility can be taken for any results or outcomes resulting from the use of this material. While every reasonable attempt has been made to provide information that is both accurate and effective, the author does not assume any responsibility for the accuracy or use/misuse of this information.

Dedication

To my Handsome son E.J and my Wonderful family for always believing in me.

Table of Contents

6

JANNIE'S BIO

When I was ten years old, I played every sport school had to offer, while saving every penny to purchase the famous Jane Fonda workout video. I've always worked out but had no idea about clean eating. When I turned forty-five, I entered my first National Physique Committee (NPC) bikini competition and that year Forever changed my life!

I have been in the fitness industry for over twenty-five years, motivating people through classes, personal training and nutrition. Because of the positive impact I've made on the lives of many people, I was featured on the Steve Harvey Show to promote my personal fitness routine. Not to mention the Creator and Inventor of My Gym Buddy Mat, a mat that protect you and your items from germs while your working out.

My training philosophy states, "Mind over matter and you can accomplish anything you set your mind to." In life all you need is the proper tools and guidance to get you where you want to be. My goal in life is to educate my clients on simple clean eating for life and attain confidence through their own personal strength.

I have also worked in the sport and physical therapy field for over fifteen years, helping Professional and College athletes reach their rehabilitation goals. This motivated me to start my own business, called Hands on Training & Therapy where I specialize in helping clients strengthen their core. I also decided to take my fitness journey to another level by establishing my own non-profit organization called the, I didn't know foundation (IDK) Specializes in teaching health and fitness to inner-city youths. I am also an ACE certified personal trainer, group fitness instructor and nutritionist health

9

coach, TRX Suspension Training Certified & CPR Certification. Currently, I can be found teaching around the world on how to LIVE AND EAT CLEAN FOR LIFE!

INTRODUCTION

I was meditating one evening and I asked God to tell me my place and purpose in life. He then answered me with this *"Help my people to take care of their temple."*

So, I immediately started to educate myself on living and eating clean for life. I started by eliminating some words from my vocabulary. One of the words I removed is the word 'diet' which I replaced with the words *'simple clean eating for life'*. I realized many people want to eat clean but don't know how or where to start.

When people approach me regarding this subject, I tell them it's really quite simple; just give up salt and sugar for two weeks. Why? Because it takes up to two weeks to change the pattern of a habit, especially one that's an *addiction.* Most of my clients' food choices contains a lot of salt and sugar. They'll go through the same withdrawals symptoms as a person who is addicted to *drugs, alcohol, nicotine or other addiction.*

This is the reason why I tell my clients not to eat fruit during this process. For example, if you eat just one grape, you will be sending a chemical message to your brain that you want more. In the same vein, that's why you shouldn't bring alcohol around an alcoholic; or tell a drug addict it's okay to smoke marijuana. This will not work! This is why I recommend practical simple steps to my clients in order to achieve a sustainable and desired change.

This workbook contains 12 simple steps which have been successful to help my clients achieve a sustainable happy weight. I am sure you will benefit as you read on.

STEP#1 CLEAN HOUSE
(TIME TO DETOX)

GET IT OUT OF YOUR HOUSE! Everything in your pantry, refrigerator and cabinets should read: ZERO SUGAR & ZERO SALT (SODIUM) Unnatural sugar is bad for you because it has unwanted calories which turn into FAT that can enter into your blood and affect your immune system which causes: obesity, diabetes, and heart disease. Too much SALT can reduce the ability for your kidneys to remove water. The results can be high blood pressure, stroke, heart failure, stomach cancer, kidney stones, bloating, puffiness and weight gain. And it doesn't stop there.

❖ Ban products high in refined sugar from your home. Keeping tempting sweets in your house will

only leave you open to sweet enticement when at your weakest moments.

❖ Prepare a food shopping list

❖ Write a plan for how you will handle your withdrawals in your Fitness Journal.

❖ Set a time to go grocery shopping and take time to **READ** your ingredients; the less words the better. For example; a package of green beans should only read green beans. And remember most of your natural meats & veggie already have natural salt & sugar.

❖ Have a plan for what you will eat in between meals.

❖ Track your measurable outcomes.

❖ Hop on the scale, get a body-fat analysis done. It can be encouraging to SEE progress being made (or lack there-of) to help reinforce your fitness plan, or to make changes to what you're doing.

❖ Eating well and KNOWING exactly what is going into your body might be the most important step in making changes to your body.

❖ Having a physical food journal is a great way to revisit what is going well and what needs adjustment to build consistency with your nutritional intake.

❖ NONFOOD REWARDS It doesn't have to be expensive or food. It could be giving yourself a candle-lit bubble bath or getting a back rub. Get creative!

RECOMMENDED INTAKE

CARBS INTAKE PER DAY

The Dietary Guidelines for Americans recommend that carbohydrates make up forty-five to sixty-five percent of your total daily calories. So, if you get 2,000 calories a day, between 900 and 1,300 calories should be from carbohydrates. That translates to between 225 and 325 grams of carbohydrates a day.

❖SUGAR INTAKE PER DAY

The first two weeks should be 15 grams or less per day.

According to the American Heart Association (AHA), the maximum amount of added sugar you should consume daily is for Men: 150 calories per day (37.5 grams or 9 teaspoons); Women: 100 calories per day (25 grams or 6 teaspoons)

❖SODIUM (SALT) INTAKE PER DAY

1500 mg of sodium amounts to 0.75 teaspoons or 3.75 grams of salt per day

Remember natural salt only.

To replace salt, you'll need those that are most flavorful and offer a nice flavorful bite like salt does. The best ones are: cayenne, paprika, black pepper, oregano, lemon peel, garlic and onion powder, and rubbed sage.

PROTEIN INTAKE PER DAY

The DRI (Dietary Reference Intake) is 0.8 grams of protein per kilogram of body weight, or 0.36 grams per pound. This amounts to: 56 grams per day for the average sedentary man and 46 grams per day for the average woman.

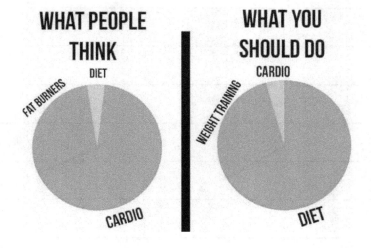

YOUR FOOD ADDICTION
Write down some of your food addictions.

NOTES:_____

_____

_____

_____

_____

_____

_____

_____

_____

_____

_____

_____

_____

READING THE NUTRITION FACTS

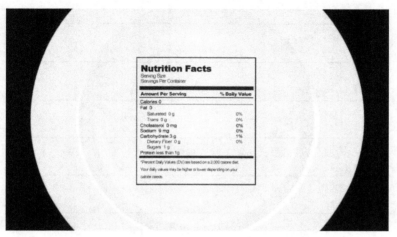

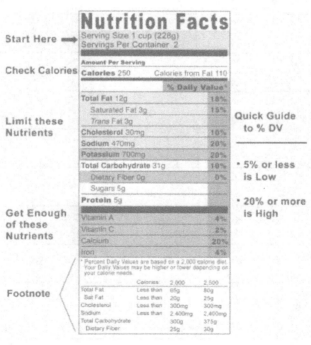

NOTES:_____

_____

_____

_____

_____

_____

_____

_____

_____

_____

_____

_____

_____

_____

21

NOTES:_____

_____

_____

_____

_____

_____

_____

_____

_____

_____

_____

_____

_____

_____

NOTES:_____

_____

_____

_____

_____

_____

_____

_____

_____

_____

_____

_____

_____

_____

STEP #2 HAVE A PLAN AND STICK TO IT!

❖ PLAN AHEAD! An action plan can help you take steps toward reaching your goal of healthier eating. Think about what eating changes will help you make healthier food choices. Get plenty of rest and be ready to start each week with an achievable goal. Note: Keep your goals realistic. Start by taking small steps toward your goals. If you feel stuck or are having a hard time, ask a friend, family member, or your doctor for help.

❖ Get motivated by creating your workout playlist. Buy new workout clothing or container sets for your meal prep. Prep Meals (Precook) prepare for the week.

❖ Keep it simple, skinless meats, No fried food and portion sizes only.

❖ Eat about six times a day, every two hours (SERVING & PORTION SIZES ONLY)

❖ Drink plenty of water. Place seven 16 oz bottles of water in each room in your house. Write numbers on each of the bottles of water and drink each before going to bed.

❖ Take a full-body photo of yourself and weigh in once a week.

❖ Schedule "ME" Time.

❖ Search Social media for helpful resources.

❖ Determine your workout schedule and exercise routine/program for the week.

WHAT IS YOUR PLAN?

NOTES:_____

_____

_____

_____

_____

_____

_____

_____

_____

_____

_____

_____

NOTES:_____
_____
_____
_____
_____
_____
_____
_____
_____
_____
_____
_____
_____
_____
_____

27

NOTES:_____

_____

_____

_____

_____

_____

_____

_____

_____

_____

_____

_____

_____

_____

28

NOTES:_____

_____

_____

_____

_____

_____

_____

_____

_____

_____

_____

_____

_____

_____

STEP #3 RECOGNIZE IT IS YOUR JOURNEY.

Get started on your fitness journey without trying to recruit anyone to join you. Just do your thing. It's your health! It's your business! So, mind it! Surround yourself with a positive support system. Let everyone know about the journey you are planning to embark on. You are about to do something amazing for yourself. The difference is, your plan is going to work! Let your spouse, kids, friends, social media acquaintances, etc. know what you're doing and how important it is to you! Let those closest to you know you need their support. If they're not on board, don't let them drag you down. You don't have to go out for junk food just because your friends are. Misery loves company.

Have a plan on how you will handle the food temptation from yourself, friends, co-workers and family.

❖ Take your focus off what your friends, family, children, co-workers etc. may or may not think about your decision.

❖ Be and think positively. No need to mention to anyone you feel like you are STARVING.

❖ Write your experiences and feelings in your journal or workbook.

❖ Stick to the plan, even if you don't feel like it.

❖ Drink Water. Thirst is often confused with hunger or food cravings.

❖ Eat More Protein. ...Distance Yourself From the Craving.

❖ Plan Your Meals. ...Avoid Getting Extremely Hungry

❖ Recognize potential temptation.

❖ **Remove yourself from temptation.**

❖ **Be honest.**

Visualize yourself resisting temptation.

❖ **Think of the long-term consequences.**

❖ **Distract yourself.**

❖ **Remember is ok to say NO THANK YOU.**

❖ **Do not give yourself a choice.**

HOW WILL YOU HANDLE TEMPTATION?

NOTES:_____

_____

_____

_____

_____

_____

_____

_____

_____

_____

_____

_____

NOTES:_____

_____

_____

_____

_____

_____

_____

_____

_____

_____

_____

_____

_____

_____

_____

34

NOTES:_____

_____

_____

_____

_____

_____

_____

_____

_____

_____

_____

_____

_____

_____

NOTES:_____

_____

_____

_____

_____

_____

_____

_____

_____

_____

_____

_____

_____

_____

NOTES:_____

_____

_____

_____

_____

_____

_____

_____

_____

_____

_____

_____

_____

_____

_____

STEP#4 ACCOUNTABILITY

Find someone you trust and tell them about your journey. Sticking to your fitness routine can be a challenge, especially if you're trying to do it alone. While some people prefer to exercise alone—and are great self-motivators—the same is not true for everyone. For many people, working out with a partner is just what they need to stay on track and reach their goals. It will help you be accountable and monitor your progress more effectively. Positive support groups are also helpful. Consider joining a gym and/or workout group or classes. If you can, a personal trainer can be extremely beneficial and effective.

WHO WILL YOU COUNT ON?

NOTES:_____

_____

_____

_____

_____

_____

_____

_____

_____

_____

_____

_____

NOTES:_____
_____
_____
_____
_____
_____
_____
_____
_____
_____
_____
_____
_____
_____
_____

40

NOTES:_____

_____

_____

_____

_____

_____

_____

_____

_____

_____

_____

_____

_____

_____

41

NOTES:_____

_____

_____

_____

_____

_____

_____

_____

_____

_____

_____

_____

_____

NOTES:_____

_____

_____

_____

_____

_____

_____

_____

_____

_____

_____

_____

_____

_____

STEP#5 EXPECT TESTS.... IT'S COMING.

❖ **How to Stop Thinking About Food and Get On With Your Day**

Do whatever it takes to STICK TO THE PLAN! You've been down this road before and so has your family, friends, and co-workers. They will cook your favorite meals and have your favorite desserts ready to serve at those holiday events, birthdays celebrations, vacation, etc. DON'T give into these temptations. It's not worth it! Love yourself. Each Day is a new day to be discipline.

❖ **It's ok to say NO THANK YOU.**

❖ **So do yourself a favor and have a small, healthful snack before dining out.**

❖ **Knock out your senses of taste and smell.**

❖ Ask yourself whether you are really hungry—or just bored.

❖ Think of calories as dollars.

❖ Prepare healthful afternoon snacks.

HOW WILL YOU HANDLE THE TEST?

NOTES:_____

_____

_____

_____

_____

_____

_____

_____

_____

_____

_____

_____

_____

_____

46

NOTES:_____

_____

_____

_____

_____

_____

_____

_____

_____

_____

_____

_____

_____

47

NOTES:

48

NOTES:_____

_____

_____

_____

_____

_____

_____

_____

_____

_____

_____

_____

_____

_____

49

NOTES:

STEP#6 GET CREATIVE

Your food will get very boring, but it only means you need to get more creative with your meals.

❖ **Cook It Yourself** Although it may require more time and effort, cooking at home with fresh food allows you to control.

❖ Use herbs and spices for flavor instead of adding salt. Spices like ginger, rosemary, cilantro, garlic or onion powder can be used to jazz up any meal.

❖ Crockpot works well.

❖ Instead of cooking egg whites in a pan, bake in a muffin pan.

❖ For egg whites and boiled eggs, throw away yolk.

❖ Use your social media and look up great ideals.

❖ Use protein bars & unsalted almonds and make a trail mix.

❖ Replace your salt with Balsamic vinegar, Lemons.

HOW WILL YOU GET CREATIVE?

NOTES:_____

_____

_____

_____

_____

_____

_____

_____

_____

_____

_____

_____

_____

53

NOTES:_____

_____

_____

_____

_____

_____

_____

_____

_____

_____

_____

_____

_____

_____

_____

54

NOTES:_____

_____

_____

_____

_____

_____

_____

_____

_____

_____

_____

_____

_____

_____

55

NOTES:_____

_____

_____

_____

_____

_____

_____

_____

_____

_____

_____

_____

_____

_____

_____

56

NOTES:_____

_____

_____

_____

_____

_____

_____

_____

_____

_____

_____

_____

_____

_____

STEP#7 ENCOURAGE YOUR-SELF.

As you lose weight, your family members, friends and co-workers may have negative comments. "In some ways, your weight loss becomes a symbol of their inability to accomplish their goals, so they may begin to act resentful -- or even mean -- oftentimes without even realizing they are doing so, "Remind them of how much their support has meant to you, and how happy you are to be healthy enough to do more things together,"

❖ They will ask questions such as:

❖ Are you sick?

❖ Why are you losing too much weight?

❖ Why are you being stuck up?

❖ Why are you not fun anymore?

❖ The only thing that matters is how you feel about your own life, behaviors, and accomplishments. Find your peace and go forth happily.

❖ Don't pay attention to the negative person.

❖ Surround yourself with positive friends.

❖ Don't feel like you owe the person an explanation.

Bottom line: LET YOUR HATERS HATE!

WHAT DO YOU LOVE ABOUT YOURSELF?

NOTES:_____

_____

_____

_____

_____

_____

_____

_____

_____

_____

_____

_____

60

NOTES:_____

_____

_____

_____

_____

_____

_____

_____

_____

_____

_____

_____

_____

_____

NOTES:_____

_____

_____

_____

_____

_____

_____

_____

_____

_____

_____

_____

_____

_____

_____

62

NOTES:_____

_____

_____

_____

_____

_____

_____

_____

_____

_____

_____

_____

_____

_____

63

NOTES:_____
_____
_____
_____
_____
_____
_____
_____
_____
_____
_____
_____
_____
_____
_____

STEP#8 LOVING THE NEW YOU! (REWARD TIME)

If you are sticking to your plan, the results will be noticed by your family, friends and co-workers. They will show interest and want to check into the CLEAN EATING REHAB.

❖ Reward ONLY if you made your personal goals.

❖ NONE EATING REWARDS.

❖ Pampering yourself massage (especially good for athletes who might not even realize how sore they really are).

❖ A fancy new body scrub, bubble bath, bath salts, or other bath.

- ❖ A really sharp-looking haircut (go to a place where the hairdresser gives you a scalp massage under the warm water as part of the process).

- ❖ A manicure or pedicure.

- ❖ Out of town spiritual & fitness events.

- ❖ Experiment with new type of workout (have you ever tried Zumba? Pilates? Swimming?)

- ❖ Explore a new park or beach that you've always driven past.

- ❖ Go to a museum or gallery that you've never visited and look around.

- ❖ Try an architecture tour or some other "tourist" type thing in your own city.

- ❖ Take a weekend trip to somewhere nearby and explore the local attractions.

HOW WILL YOU REWARD YOURSELF?

NOTES:_____

_____

_____

_____

_____

_____

_____

_____

_____

_____

_____

_____

67

NOTES:_____

_____

_____

_____

_____

_____

_____

_____

_____

_____

_____

_____

_____

_____

_____

_____

68

NOTES:_____

_____

_____

_____

_____

_____

_____

_____

_____

_____

_____

_____

_____

_____

NOTES:_____
_____
_____
_____
_____
_____
_____
_____
_____
_____
_____
_____
_____
_____
_____
_____

70

NOTES:_____
_____
_____
_____
_____
_____
_____
_____
_____
_____
_____
_____
_____
_____

STEP#9 DON'T LET IT GET TO YOUR HEAD.

Enjoy the compliments, how you look and most of all the extra energy, but never lose focus of your goals. *WARNING: TOO MANY COMPLIMENTS MAY CAUSE A RELAPSE!*

❖ How do you stay focused when losing weight?

❖ Focus on gradual loss…

❖ Focus on nutrition. Exercise is important…

❖ Become aware of your hunger…

❖ Eat when you're hungry…

❖ Drink lots of water...

❖ Keep healthy options available...

HOW WILL YOU STAY FOCUS?

NOTES:_____

_____

_____

_____

_____

_____

_____

_____

_____

_____

_____

_____

_____

73

NOTES:_____

_____

_____

_____

_____

_____

_____

_____

_____

_____

_____

_____

_____

_____

74

NOTES:_____

_____

_____

_____

_____

_____

_____

_____

_____

_____

_____

_____

_____

_____

75

NOTES:_____
_____
_____
_____
_____
_____
_____
_____
_____
_____
_____
_____
_____
_____
_____

76

NOTES:_____

_____

_____

_____

_____

_____

_____

_____

_____

_____

_____

_____

_____

_____

STEP#10 LISTEN TO YOUR BODY

Remember, your body will talk to you and you should listen to it.

❖ Pay attention to how your clothes fit.

❖ Pay attention to how your jewelry fits.

❖ Pay attention to how your belt fits.

❖ Pay attention to swollen Swelling in strange places ankles, fingers, face, and stomach, swelling could mean you're consuming too much salt or sugar.

❖ Persistent thirst....

❖ You find food bland and boring.

❖ Frequent mild headaches.

❖ High blood Pressure.

❖ Your tired but Problem sleeping.

❖ You crave for salty or sugar foods.

❖ Your mood is all over the place.

When you eat a lot of salt & sugar, your hormones react immediately. You get a spike of insulin and serotonin, your happy hormone, followed by a huge crash of both. You feel sluggish and your mood plummets, causing you to crave more sugar and "emotionally eat" or just feel depressed and awful until your next meal.

NOTES:_____

_____

_____

_____

_____

_____

_____

_____

_____

_____

_____

_____

_____

_____

_____

80

NOTES:_____

_____

_____

_____

_____

_____

_____

_____

_____

_____

_____

_____

_____

_____

81

NOTES:_____

_____

_____

_____

_____

_____

_____

_____

_____

_____

_____

_____

_____

_____

_____

NOTES:_____

_____

_____

_____

_____

_____

_____

_____

_____

_____

_____

_____

_____

_____

_____

83

NOTES:_____

_____

_____

_____

_____

_____

_____

_____

_____

_____

_____

_____

_____

_____

STEP#11 REMEMBER WHEN

❖ **Remember the hard work…**

❖ **Surround yourself with positivity. …**

❖ **Create a vision board. …**

❖ **Create a mental image of a future you. …**

❖ **Remember how your friends, family, co-workers no-tice first.**

❖ **Make specific, realistic goals with deadlines…**

❖ **Remember to reward yourself. …**

❖ **Be kind to yourself and acknowledge your positive attributes, as well as progress…**

❖ **Don't compare yourself to others…**

❖ **Remember how you felt…**

85

❖ Remember your struggles...Remember the twelve steps...

❖ Remember when you didn't have the energy...

❖ Remember the BEFORE photos...

❖ Remember to go back to your Journal...

BIGGEST CHALLENGE YOU'VE OVERCOME?

NOTES:_____

_____

_____

_____

_____

_____

_____

_____

_____

_____

_____

_____

87

NOTES:_____

_____

_____

_____

_____

_____

_____

_____

_____

_____

_____

_____

_____

_____

88

NOTES:_____

_____

_____

_____

_____

_____

_____

_____

_____

_____

_____

_____

_____

_____

NOTES:_____

_____

_____

_____

_____

_____

_____

_____

_____

_____

_____

_____

_____

_____

_____

90

NOTES:

STEP#12 TELL YOUR STORY

❖ Be proud of your Accomplishments.

❖ Encourage others by sharing your story.

❖ Review your fitness journal.

❖ Appreciate how far you have come.

❖ Share your clean eating experience.

❖ Reward Self

MACROS

What is a "Macronutrient" Anyway?

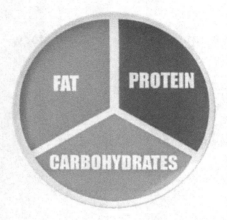

"To macro" means tracking the number of grams of protein, carbohydrates, and fats you consume on a particular day.

Counting macros for weight loss, you'll want to make sure you're counting macros in such a way that you're also cutting calories. PORTION CONTROL

KEEP IT SIMPLE

EASY
PORTION CONTROL

PROTEIN SERVING = PALM
Women = 1 palm (20-30g protein)
Men = 2 palms (40-60g protein)

CARB SERVING = CUPED HAND
Women = 1 cupped hand (40-60g carbs)
Men = 2 cupped hands (40-60g carbs)

VEGETABLE SERVING = FIST
Women = 1 fist
Men = 2 fists

FAT SERVING = THUMB
Women = 1 thumb (7-12g fat)
Men = 2 tumbs (15-25g fat)

94

NOTES:_____

_____

_____

_____

_____

_____

_____

_____

_____

_____

_____

_____

_____

_____

NOTES:_____

_____

_____

_____

_____

_____

_____

_____

_____

_____

_____

_____

_____

_____

YOUR WEEKLY MEAL PLAN

Date: _____

Weekly Meal Plan

	Sunday	Monday	Tuesday	Wednesday	Thursday	Friday	Saturday
Breakfast							
Snack							
Lunch							
Snack							
Dinner							

Date: _____

Weekly Meal Plan

	Sunday	Monday	Tuesday	Wednesday	Thursday	Friday	Saturday
Breakfast							
Snack							
Lunch							
Snack							
Dinner							

Date: _____

Weekly Meal Plan

	Sunday	Monday	Tuesday	Wednesday	Thursday	Friday	Saturday
Breakfast							
Snack							
Lunch							
Snack							
Dinner							

Date: _____

Weekly Meal Plan

	Sunday	Monday	Tuesday	Wednesday	Thursday	Friday	Saturday
Breakfast							
Snack							
Lunch							
Snack							
Dinner							

Date: _____

Weekly Meal Plan

	Sunday	Monday	Tuesday	Wednesday	Thursday	Friday	Saturday
Breakfast							
Snack							
Lunch							
Snack							
Dinner							

BEGINNER'S WORKOUT ROUTINE

Push yourself to try something that's high impact and low impact as well as low intensity and high intensity and see what gets you pumped and excited. What type of workout environment makes you feel the most confident and comfortable?

❖ **Training Frequency: 3 days & increase to 5 days per week.**

❖ **Training Days: Monday, Wednesday, Friday and increase as you get stronger.**

❖ **Routine Duration: 3 to 6 months (change routine)**

❖ **Sets Per Exercise: 2 to 3 sets.**

❖ **Rest Between Sets: Up to 2 minutes.**

YOUR WORKOUT LOG

WORKOUT LOG

GOALS: _____

Track your fitness and strength training progress.

	M Tu W Th F Sa Su	M Tu W Th F Sa Su	M Tu W Th F Sa Su	M Tu W Th F Sa Su	M Tu W Th F Sa
DATE:					
WEIGHT:					
SLEEP (hrs):					
CALORIES:					
TIME (minutes):					
NOTES:					

EXERCISES	1RM*	SETS REPS WT	SETS REPS WT	SETS REPS WT	SETS REPS WT	SETS REPS W

*1RM – One Rep Max (for reference)

CARDIO EXERCISES	TIME DIST INT**	TIME DIST INT	TIME DIST INT	TIME DIST INT	TIME DIST I

WORKOUT LOG

GOALS: _____

Track your fitness and strength training progress.

	M Tu W Th F Sa Su	M Tu W Th F Sa Su	M Tu W Th F Sa Su	M Tu W Th F Sa Su	M Tu W Th F Sa
DATE:					
WEIGHT:					
SLEEP (hr):					
CALORIES:					
TIME (minutes):					
NOTES:					

EXERCISES	1RM*	SETS	REPS	WT	SETS	REPS	WT	SETS	REPS	WT	SETS	REPS	WT	SETS	REPS	V

*1RM –One Rep Max (for reference)

CARDIO EXERCISES	TIME	DIST	INT**	TIME	DIST	INT	TIME	DIST	INT	TIME	DIST	INT	TIME	DIST	I

WORKOUT LOG

GOALS: _____

Track your fitness and strength training progress.

		M Tu W Th F Sa Su	M Tu W Th F Sa Su	M Tu W Th F Sa Su	M Tu W Th F Sa Su	M Tu W Th F Sa
DATE:						

WEIGHT: _____ _____ _____ _____ _____
SLEEP (hrs): _____ _____ _____ _____ _____
CALORIES: _____ _____ _____ _____ _____
TIME (minutes): _____ _____ _____ _____ _____

NOTES:

EXERCISES	1RM*	SETS	REPS	WT	SETS	REPS	WT	SETS	REPS	WT	SETS	REPS	WT	SETS	REPS	W

*1RM – One Rep Max (for reference)

CARDIO EXERCISES	TIME	DIST	INT**	TIME	DIST	INT	TIME	DIST	INT	TIME	DIST	INT	TIME	DIST	I

WORKOUT LOG

GOALS: _____

Track your fitness and strength training progress.

	M Tu W Th F Sa Su	M Tu W Th F Sa Su	M Tu W Th F Sa Su	M Tu W Th F Sa Su	M Tu W Th F Sa
DATE:					
WEIGHT:					
SLEEP (hrs):					
CALORIES:					
TIME (minutes):					
NOTES:					

EXERCISES	1RM*	SETS	REPS	WT	SETS	REPS	WT	SETS	REPS	WT	SETS	REPS	WT	SETS	REPS	V

*1RM – One Rep Max (for reference)

CARDIO EXERCISES	TIME	DIST	INT*	TIME	DIST	INT	TIME	DIST	INT	TIME	DIST	INT	TIME	DIST	I

WORKOUT LOG

GOALS: _____

Track your fitness and strength training progress.

		M Tu W Th F Sa Su	M Tu W Th F Sa Su	M Tu W Th F Sa Su	M Tu W Th F Sa Su	M Tu W Th F Sa
DATE:						
WEIGHT:						
SLEEP (hrs):						
CALORIES:						
TIME (minutes):						
NOTES:						

EXERCISES	1RM*	SETS	REPS	WT	SETS	REPS	WT	SETS	REPS	WT	SETS	REPS	WT	SETS	REPS	W

*1RM –One Rep Max (for reference)

CARDIO EXERCISES	TIME	DIST	INT**	TIME	DIST	INT	TIME	DIST	INT	TIME	DIST	INT	TIME	DIST	I

BODY CHART

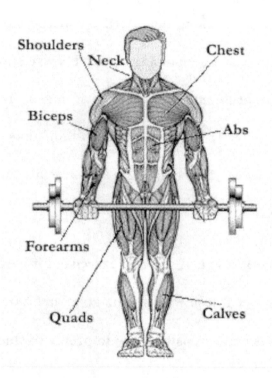

UNDERSTANDING SIMPLE PLANKS FOR LIFE!
CORE AND ABS.

❖ Planks cost nothing, you need no special equipment and they can be done anywhere. They're super easy to incorporate into a workout or even your daily routine. ... They're so simple you can do planks on your living room floor during commercials or work breaks.

❖ The plank is one of the best exercises for core conditioning but it also works your glute and hamstrings, supports proper posture, and improves balance.

❖ Planks for Beginners. Use a mat or towel to rest your knees on as you come to all fours. Step your hands out until you're in a modified plank position, hands directly beneath your shoulders and elbows in. Engage your stomach and glutes, holding for 15 to 30 seconds. Perform three rounds of 15 to 30 second holds.

❖ Planks are one of those exercises that will never go out of style.

Plant the hands directly under the shoulders (slightly wider than shoulder-width apart) like you're about to do a push-up.

Elbow Plank

Ball Plank Reverse

BAND EXERCISES

Is a great addition to any strength training routine or rehabilitation program and come in a variety of sizes, lengths, and strengths. ... Just like free weights, exercise bands come in a range of resistance levels, from highly stretchable to heavy-duty strength.

Free weights are also more versatile than machines because they allow for more variations in the range of motion. Free weights require balance, and they tend to promote more activity of the joint stabilizer muscles. You can perform a complete strength training routine with a few dumbbells, and a little imagination.

SIMPLE BALL EXERCISE

An exercise ball, also known as a Swiss Ball, is a ball constructed of soft elastic with a diameter of approximately 35 to 85 centimeters and filled with air. The air pressure is changed by removing a valve stem and either filling with air or letting the ball deflate.

The exercise ball is one of the best tools for building strength, endurance, and stability in the core. Because you're on an unstable surface

WHY BE PHYSICALLY ACTIVE.

Strengthens your heart, lungs, bones and muscles. Gives you more energy and strength. Helps control your weight and blood pressure. ... Pleasure dancing and home exercise More vigorous physical activity can further improve the fitness of your heart and lungs.

Physical activity helps: Prevent and better control some risk factors for heart disease: blood cholesterol, diabetes and hypertension. Improve muscle and bone health (osteoporosis prevention) Improve sleep.

Physical activity or exercise can improve your health and reduce the risk of developing several diseases like type 2 diabetes, cancer and cardiovascular disease. Physical activity and exercise can have immediate and long-term health benefits. Most importantly, regular activity can improve your quality of life.

5-DAY CARDIO WORKOUT PLAN

❖ Jump ropes.

❖ Moderate-intensity exercise on cardio machine 1: 10 minutes.

❖ Bodyweight squats with a pause at the bottom: 10 reps.

❖ Push-ups: 10 reps.

❖ Planks: 30 to 60 seconds.

❖ Jump rope: 1 minute.

❖ Rest 30 seconds.

❖ High-intensity exercise on cardio machine.

JUMPING ROPE IS A GREAT CALORIE-BURNER.

❖ You'd have to run an eight-minute miles to work off more calories than you'd burn jumping rope. This same size person burns about 815 calories running at 6 mph for 60 minutes. Simply put, if you jump rope at a fast pace, and run at a slow pace, you will burn more fat jumping rope. With both forms of exercise, people who are bigger will burn more calories.

❖ Jumping rope and running are both aerobic activities, benefiting your heart and lungs, exercising your large muscles and building endurance. ... Eventually, your heart and lungs become stronger and more efficient. Jumping rope can replace running.

❖ A good jump rope is one of the best investments you can make in your own fitness because it is an extremely effective form of cardiorespiratory exercise and doesn't require much more than a little space, a timer and some creativity. Humans burn about five calories to consume 1 liter of oxygen.

REMEMBER TO STRETCH

It is better to stretch after a workout Static stretching before exercise can weaken performance, such as sprint speed, in studies. The most likely reason is that holding the stretch tires out your muscles. You should warm up by doing dynamic stretches, which are like your workout but at a lower intensity.

NOTES:_____

_____

_____

_____

_____

_____

_____

_____

_____

_____

_____

_____

_____

_____

_____

_____

NOTES:_____

_____

_____

_____

_____

_____

_____

_____

_____

_____

_____

_____

_____

_____

NOTES:_____

_____

_____

_____

_____

_____

_____

_____

_____

_____

_____

_____

_____

_____

_____

122

NOTES:_____
_____
_____
_____
_____
_____
_____
_____
_____
_____
_____
_____
_____
_____
_____

123

NOTES:_____

_____

_____

_____

_____

_____

_____

_____

_____

_____

_____

_____

_____

_____

_____

_____

NOTES:_____

_____

_____

_____

_____

_____

_____

_____

_____

_____

_____

_____

_____

_____

_____

125

NOTES:_____

_____

_____

_____

_____

_____

_____

_____

_____

_____

_____

_____

_____

_____

_____

_____

126

NOTES:_____

_____

_____

_____

_____

_____

_____

_____

_____

_____

_____

_____

_____

_____

_____

YOUR SHOPPING LIST

Shopping List

Notes:

Shopping List

Notes:

Shopping List

Notes:

YOUR WEIGHT IN CHART

MONTH 1	DATE	WEIGHT	Remarks	
Week 1			❑ I lost a little weight!	❑ It's too early to tell!
Week 2			❑ Progress!	❑ No weight loss yet
Week 3			❑ I lost weight!	❑ No weight loss this week
Week 4			❑ Doing well	❑ I'll try harder

MONTH 2	DATE	WEIGHT	Remarks (pick from bottom of page or write your own)
Week 5			
Week 6			
Week 7			
Week 8			

MONTH 3	DATE	WEIGHT	Remarks
Week 9			
Week 10			
Week 11			
Week 12			

MONTH 4	DATE	WEIGHT	Remarks
Week 13			
Week 14			
Week 15			
Week 16			

MONTH 5	DATE	WEIGHT	Remarks
Week 17			
Week 18			
Week 19			
Week 20			

MONTH 1	DATE	WEIGHT	Remarks	
Week 1			❏ I lost a little weight!	❏ It's too early to tell!
Week 2			❏ Progress!	❏ No weight loss yet
Week 3			❏ I lost weight!	❏ No weight loss this week
Week 4			❏ Doing well	❏ I'll try harder

MONTH 2	DATE	WEIGHT	Remarks (pick from bottom of page or write your own)
Week 5			
Week 6			
Week 7			
Week 8			

MONTH 3	DATE	WEIGHT	Remarks
Week 9			
Week 10			
Week 11			
Week 12			

MONTH 4	DATE	WEIGHT	Remarks
Week 13			
Week 14			
Week 15			
Week 16			

MONTH 5	DATE	WEIGHT	Remarks
Week 17			
Week 18			
Week 19			
Week 20			

MONTH 1	DATE	WEIGHT	Remarks	
Week 1			❑ I lost a little weight!	❑ It's too early to tell!
Week 2			❑ Progress!	❑ No weight loss yet
Week 3			❑ I lost weight!	❑ No weight loss this week
Week 4			❑ Doing well	❑ I'll try harder

MONTH 2	DATE	WEIGHT	Remarks (pick from bottom of page or write your own)
Week 5			
Week 6			
Week 7			
Week 8			

MONTH 3	DATE	WEIGHT	Remarks
Week 9			
Week 10			
Week 11			
Week 12			

MONTH 4	DATE	WEIGHT	Remarks
Week 13			
Week 14			
Week 15			
Week 16			

MONTH 5	DATE	WEIGHT	Remarks
Week 17			
Week 18			
Week 19			
Week 20			

MONTH 1	DATE	WEIGHT	Remarks	
Week 1			❏ I lost a little weight!	❏ It's too early to tell!
Week 2			❏ Progress!	❏ No weight loss yet
Week 3			❏ I lost weight!	❏ No weight loss this week
Week 4			❏ Doing well	❏ I'll try harder

MONTH 2	DATE	WEIGHT	Remarks (pick from bottom of page or write your own)
Week 5			
Week 6			
Week 7			
Week 8			

MONTH 3	DATE	WEIGHT	Remarks
Week 9			
Week 10			
Week 11			
Week 12			

MONTH 4	DATE	WEIGHT	Remarks
Week 13			
Week 14			
Week 15			
Week 16			

MONTH 5	DATE	WEIGHT	Remarks
Week 17			
Week 18			
Week 19			
Week 20			

MONTH 1	DATE	WEIGHT	Remarks	
Week 1			❏ I lost a little weight!	❏ It's too early to tell!
Week 2			❏ Progress!	❏ No weight loss yet
Week 3			❏ I lost weight!	❏ No weight loss this week
Week 4			❏ Doing well	❏ I'll try harder

MONTH 2	DATE	WEIGHT	Remarks (pick from bottom of page or write your own)
Week 5			
Week 6			
Week 7			
Week 8			

MONTH 3	DATE	WEIGHT	Remarks
Week 9			
Week 10			
Week 11			
Week 12			

MONTH 4	DATE	WEIGHT	Remarks
Week 13			
Week 14			
Week 15			
Week 16			

MONTH 5	DATE	WEIGHT	Remarks
Week 17			
Week 18			
Week 19			
Week 20			

MONTH 1	DATE	WEIGHT	Remarks	
Week 1			❑ I lost a little weight!	❑ It's too early to tell!
Week 2			❑ Progress!	❑ No weight loss yet
Week 3			❑ I lost weight!	❑ No weight loss this week
Week 4			❑ Doing well	❑ I'll try harder

MONTH 2	DATE	WEIGHT	Remarks (pick from bottom of page or write your own)
Week 5			
Week 6			
Week 7			
Week 8			

MONTH 3	DATE	WEIGHT	Remarks
Week 9			
Week 10			
Week 11			
Week 12			

MONTH 4	DATE	WEIGHT	Remarks
Week 13			
Week 14			
Week 15			
Week 16			

MONTH 5	DATE	WEIGHT	Remarks
Week 17			
Week 18			
Week 19			
Week 20			

MONTH 1	DATE	WEIGHT	Remarks	
Week 1			❏ I lost a little weight!	❏ It's too early to tell!
Week 2			❏ Progress!	❏ No weight loss yet
Week 3			❏ I lost weight!	❏ No weight loss this week
Week 4			❏ Doing well	❏ I'll try harder

MONTH 2	DATE	WEIGHT	Remarks (pick from bottom of page or write your own)
Week 5			
Week 6			
Week 7			
Week 8			

MONTH 3	DATE	WEIGHT	Remarks
Week 9			
Week 10			
Week 11			
Week 12			

MONTH 4	DATE	WEIGHT	Remarks
Week 13			
Week 14			
Week 15			
Week 16			

MONTH 5	DATE	WEIGHT	Remarks
Week 17			
Week 18			
Week 19			
Week 20			

137

NOTES:

138

NOTES:_____

_____

_____

_____

_____

_____

_____

_____

_____

_____

_____

_____

_____

_____

139

NOTES:_____

_____

_____

_____

_____

_____

_____

_____

_____

_____

_____

_____

_____

_____

_____

NOTES:_____

_____

_____

_____

_____

_____

_____

_____

_____

_____

_____

_____

_____

_____

NOTES:_____
_____
_____
_____
_____
_____
_____
_____
_____
_____
_____
_____
_____
_____
_____

NOTES:_____
_____
_____
_____
_____
_____
_____
_____
_____
_____
_____
_____
_____
_____

143

NOTES:_____

_____

_____

_____

_____

_____

_____

_____

_____

_____

_____

_____

_____

_____

144

NOTES:_____

_____

_____

_____

_____

_____

_____

_____

_____

_____

_____

_____

_____

_____

145

NOTES:_____

_____

_____

_____

_____

_____

_____

_____

_____

_____

_____

_____

_____

_____

_____

_____

CPSIA information can be obtained
at www.ICGtesting.com
Printed in the USA
LVHW041316201119
637825LV00007B/761/P

9 780578 445892